A Job For Pop

Maverick
Early Readers

'A Job for Pop'

An original concept by Jenny Jinks

© Jenny Jinks

Illustrated by Gina Lorena Maldonado

Published by MAVERICK ARTS PUBLISHING LTD

Studio 3A, City Business Centre, 6 Brighton Road,

Horsham, West Sussex, RH13 5BB

© Maverick Arts Publishing Limited August 2018

+44 (0)1403 256941

A CIP catalogue record for this book is available at the British Library.

ISBN 978-1-84886-369-9

www.maverickbooks.co.uk

Blue

This book is rated as: Blue Band (Guided Reading)
This story is decodable at Letters and Sounds Phase 4.

A Job For Pop

by Jenny Jinks

illustrated by Gina Lorena Maldonado

Pop was a pirate.

But he was getting a bit too old.

CRASH!

"I have to stop," said Pop.

"I am not a good pirate."

So Pop left his ship and went to town.

But town was not like Pop's ship.

"Ahoy there!" said Pop.

But no one ever said it back.

"X marks the spot!" said Pop.

The town was a mess.

Pop got a job in the bank.

But he was not good at it.

Pop got a job on a boat.

But he was not good at it.

Pop got a job on a bus, but he got lost.

He kept ending up at the seaside!

Now Pop had no job.

23

Pop sat in the park. He felt sad.

Then Pop got a job that was
perfect for him.

25

Pop did lots of digging.

Soon the park was looking good.

Pop felt like a pirate again.

He had a ship, and he had

lots of pirates to have fun with.

Quiz

1. What is Pop?
a) A king
b) A wizard
c) A pirate

2. What sound does the ship make when it hits land?
a) Crash!
b) Boom!
c) Ping!

3. Where does Pop go?
a) To town
b) To a lighthouse
c) To another ship

4. What is Pop's perfect job?

a) A bus driver

b) A park keeper

c) A tooth fairy

5. What does Pop love to do?

a) Paint

b) Stroke cats

c) Dig holes

Turn over for answers

Book Bands for Guided Reading

The Institute of Education book banding system is a scale of colours that reflects the various levels of reading difficulty. The bands are assigned by taking into account the content, the language style, the layout and phonics.

Maverick Early Readers are a bright, attractive range of books covering the pink to purple bands. All of these books have been book banded for guided reading to the industry standard and edited by a leading educational consultant.

Pink

Red

Yellow

Blue

Green

Orange

Turquoise

Purple

Gold

White

To view the whole Maverick Readers scheme, visit our website at

www.maverickearlyreaders.com

Or scan the QR code above to view our scheme instantly!

Quiz Answers: 1c, 2a, 3a, 4b, 5c